Explode The Code 8

Nancy Hall
Rena Price

Educators Publishing Service, Inc.
Cambridge, Mass. 02138

Cover by Hugh Price

Text illustrations by Jamie Maxfield

June 2001 Printing   ISBN 0-8388-1647-9

CONTENTS

Lesson 1

A **suffix** is an ending added to a root to change the meaning slightly.
-ness and **-less** are suffixes.

Circle the suffixes and write the syllables in the squares.

1.	kind(ness)	*kind*	*ness* 2
2.	thankfulness	— — — — —	— — —	— — — —
3.	bottomless	— — —	— — —	— — — —
4.	wilderness	— — —	— — —	— — — —
5.	regardless	— —	— — — —	— — — —
6.	foolishness	— — — —	— — —	— — — —
7.	helpfulness	— — — —	— — —	— — — —

Now count the syllables in each word and write the number in the margin. (Tap the desk to help yourself hear the syllables.)

2

Unscramble the syllables to make a word that fits the meaning.

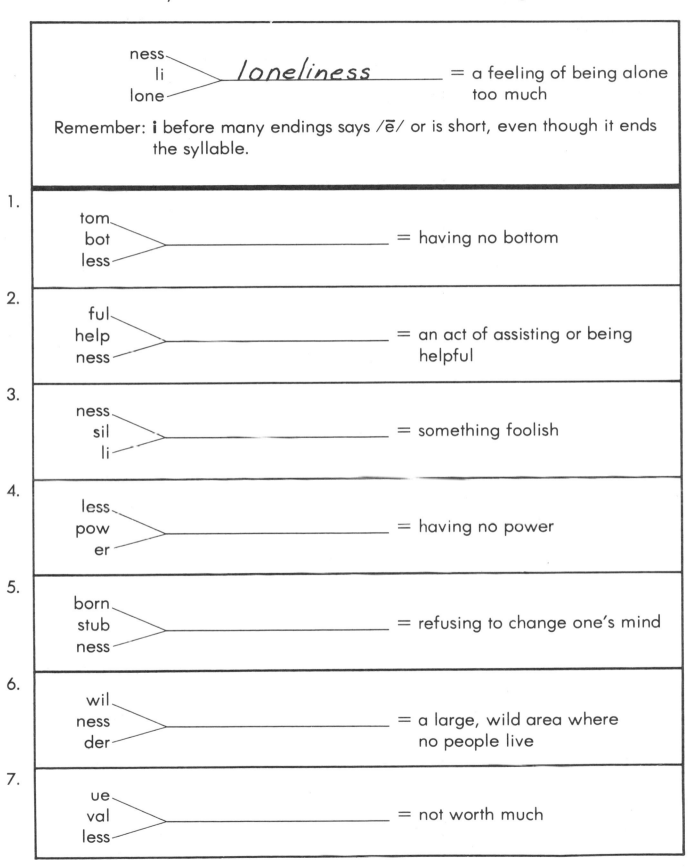

ness
li
lone
loneliness = a feeling of being alone too much

Remember: **i** before many endings says /ē/ or is short, even though it ends the syllable.

1.
tom
bot
less
= having no bottom

2.
ful
help
ness
= an act of assisting or being helpful

3.
ness
sil
li
= something foolish

4.
less
pow
er
= having no power

5.
born
stub
ness
= refusing to change one's mind

6.
wil
ness
der
= a large, wild area where no people live

7.
ue
val
less
= not worth much

Roots and Suffixes: Circle the roots and complete the sentences with the words.

(stubborn) (stubborn)ness	Tracy is a very _stubborn_ girl. Her _Stubbornness_ often gets her into trouble. Note: When the root ends in **e**, it usually drops the **e** when the suffix begins with a vowel (strange + er = stranger). When the root ends in **y**, the **y** changes to **i** when you add a suffix (gloomy + ness = gloominess).	
1.	stranger strangeness	There was a _____ about the old house that made even a _____ shiver.
2.	polite politeness	_____ is something that teachers like. If you are _____, they will often praise you.
3.	noise noiseless	A buzzing fly makes a lot of _____. I wish someone would develop a _____ fly.
4.	value valueless	Many people put great _____ on their cars. I have an old rusted jeep that is _____, but I love it anyway.
5.	slippery slipperiness	The _____ of the icy sidewalks made it too _____ to walk without boots.
6.	gloomy gloominess	The _____ of the day began to affect us all. Why can't the sun shine on such a _____ day?
7.	reckless recklessness	Eric was a very _____ bike rider. His _____ caused him to smash into his mother's parked car.

Antonyms: Find the word that means the opposite of the given word and write it in the boxes.

A word that means the opposite is called an **antonym**.

weightless	kindness	smoothness
rudeness	careless	helpfulness
hopeless	fearless	emptiness

1.

Roughness: `s m o o t h n e s s`

2.

Cruelty:

3.

Careful:

4.

Politeness:

5.

Heavy:

6.

Fullness:

7.

Afraid:

Circle the correct words below.

> Look at the suffix **-less** and think about the words we have used with this suffix. A sleeveless dress is one _____ sleeves. You now know that the suffix **-less** means "_____."
>
> **-ness** means "a state of being"; for example, **happiness** means "being happy."

1. When you have been home alone for a long time, might you feel a sense of

   (loneliness)   or   largeness?

2. When you cannot change something that has happened and you wish you could, might you feel

   powerless   or   politeness?

3. It is a splendid day with sun and blue sky. Would you describe the day as

   countless   or   cloudless?

4. When you taste a piece of lemon and it makes you wrinkle your nose, is it

   the sourness   or   the snugness?

5. On a windy, stormy night a huge tree blew down near your house but nothing was hurt. Do you have a feeling of

   thanklessness   or   thankfulness?

6. It has rained all week and even the towels and the sheets on your bed feel wet. Is what you feel in the air

   deafness   or   dampness?

7. The dog and cat get into a fight and tip over Mom's best vase, smashing it to bits. Mom is angry when she gets home. Are you

   blameless   or   softness?

Check the headline that matches each picture.

1.		☑ Mouse Powerless with Cat ☐ Dog's Politeness Wins Cat
2.		☐ Brainless Idea Helps Humankind ☐ Brightness Comes from Many Windows
3.		☐ Glassy Ice Cream Wins for Smoothness ☐ Grassy Hill Chosen for Festival
4.		☐ Stubbornness of Mule — Can't Be Budged ☐ Steepness of Road Makes for a Hard Race
5.		☐ Reckless Driver Arrested for Speeding ☐ Reckless Tail Sweeps Table Top
6.		☐ Pete Powerless to Stop Earthquake ☐ Helpfulness of Pet Stops Burglar
7.		☐ Kindness to Others Is Rewarded ☐ Carelessness Results in Lost Bracelet

Yes or No?

		Yes	No
1.	Is it foolishness to help a friend?	☐	☑
2.	If your full cup is bottomless, will you ever be thirsty?	☐	☐
3.	Can you get holes in the elbows of a sleeveless sweater?	☐	☐
4.	Is the wilderness slowly being destroyed by humans?	☐	☐
5.	When you help your friend do her homework, is it kindness?	☐	☐
6.	If you slam your sister's fingers in the door, would she praise your politeness?	☐	☐
7.	Is it careless to leave your new bike in the middle of the driveway?	☐	☐

Rena's Cool Idea

It was a hot, cloudless, muggy day in July. Not a single leaf was moving, and dampness hung in the air. The flies buzzed slowly; it was very humid. Too hot to move! Even swimming in the pool was foolishness; it was so hot! Everyone and everything drooped. But not Rena! She picked up her wireless walkie-talkie and ordered, "A truckload, please."

Her craziness turned out to be helpfulness when a truck arrived to dump five hundred pounds of ice into the swimming pool. Rena and her friends were the only ones to enjoy any coolness that day!

1. Circle all the words that end with the suffix **-ness** or **-less**.

2. Underline the words that tell why this day was so bad.

3. When you have a problem like Rena's and you don't know how to solve it,

   you feel h__ __ __ less.

4. Would you praise Rena for her rudeness or her smartness? (Circle one.)

5. If you had been Rena, what would you have done? (Circle one.)

   a. Blamed the weather forecaster for not warning you?

   b. Rung the fire alarm to let your friends know about the burning heat?

   c. Rubbed your skin with frozen ice cream cones?

   d. Other _____

   _____

Some suffixes do not sound like their spelling.
-ous says /us/ as in **famous**.   **-or** says /er/ as in **sailor**.

Circle the suffixes and write the syllables in the squares.

Note: Sometimes the way you divide a word into syllables is different from the way you divide it into a root and suffix.

1.	act(or)		_a c_	_t o r_ 2
2.	inventor	— —	— — —	— — —
3.	marvelous	— — —	— — —	— — —
4.	spectator	— — — —	— —	— — —
5.	advisor	— —	— —	— — —
6.	glamorous	— — — —	— —	— — —
7.	nervous		— — —	— — — —

Now count the syllables in each word and write the number in the margin.
Remember to tap!

10

Unscramble the syllables to make a word that fits the meaning.

one who collects things = col / tor / lec → *collector*

1. very large or great = dous / men / tre → _____

2. one who inspects things = spec / in / tor → _____

3. very funny = mor / hu / ous → _____

4. willing to give; unselfish = gen / ous / er → _____

5. a college teacher = pro / sor / fes → _____

6. someone who comes to see someone = tor / vis / i → _____

7. full of poison = ous / son / poi → _____

Roots and Suffixes: Circle the roots and complete the sentences with the words.

| (poison) (poisonous) | If you dump _poisonous_ waste into lakes and rivers, it will _poison_ the water you drink. |

1.
| conduct conductor | The _____ raised her baton and started to _____ the band. |

2.
| mountain mountainous | The _____ state of Nevada does not have a single _____ in the south. |

3.
| hazard hazardous | Doctors say, "Smoking is _____ to your health." Is drinking also a _____? |

4.
| act actor | The _____ closed his eyes and began to weep. He can _____ well. |

5.
| invent inventor | Thomas Edison was a famous _____. He worked long hours to _____ the electric light. |

6.
| humor humorous | Greta has a good sense of _____. She always tells stories in a most _____ way. |

7.
| edit editor | An _____ is someone who will _____, or correct, the book you have written. |

Definitions: Find the word that is described and write it in the boxes.

Remember: **-ous** says /us/.

governor	continuous	instructor
enormous	ridiculous	nervous
mountainous	spectator	collector

1. Someone who gets upset and worries easily is said to be:

2. The person who runs or governs the state:

3. Something that continues on and never stops is said to be:

4. A person who watches sports events:

5. Something that is very large is said to be:

6. A person who teaches you:

7. Something that is foolish and might be made fun of is said to be:

Circle the correct words below.

Look at the suffix **-or** and think about the words we have used with this suffix. An actor is a _____ who acts. You now know that **-or** usually means "a _____ who does something."

1. If you correct a book before it's published, are you

   a sailor   or   an editor?

2. When you want to share what you have with someone else, are you

   curious   or   generous?

3. When you give someone advice and help them decide what to do, are you

   an elevator   or   an advisor?

4. When you look something over carefully to see if it is running properly, are you

   an inspector   or   a tractor?

5. If you are directing a play and telling the actors what to do, are you

   the director   or   the professor?

6. If you are very handsome and charming, are you

   enormous   or   glamorous?

7. If you are very angry at someone for something they did, are you

   fabulous   or   furious?

Check the headline that matches each picture.

#	Picture	Headlines
1.		☐ Mountainous Region Hit by Fire ☐ Marvelous Story Told by Mayor
2.		☐ Glamorous Visitor Gets Wet ☐ Generous Donor Gives Rare Fossil
3.		☐ Poisonous Gas Kills Tiger ☐ Furious Workers Demand More Money
4.		☐ Continuous Show by Shooting Stars ☐ Conductor Travels by Steamship
5.		☐ Inventor Discovers Constant Sunlight ☐ Inventor Covers Son with Invisible Paint
6.		☐ Author Writes New Book ☐ Author Wades in Cool Brook
7.		☐ Spectators Cheer Team ☐ Enormous Mudslide Stops Traffic

Yes or No?

		Yes	No
1.	Is an actor a famous person?	☐	☐
2.	Will a visitor stay at home?	☐	☐
3.	If you are generous, will you give your friend a sandwich?	☐	☐
4.	Will a governor be the conductor of a band?	☐	☐
5.	If the land is mountainous, can it also be enormous?	☐	☐
6.	Is it foolish to use poisonous spray around birds and wildlife?	☐	☐
7.	If you are curious, will you get into bed and pull the covers over your head?	☐	☐

Don't Be a Show-off

Climbing trees can be very hazardous even if you know what you're doing. I was a fabulous tree climber and swinger as a girl. It was a marvelous feeling to swing out on a branch and see how far I could jump down. My pals and I played this game for hours in a big apple tree.

One day I decided to climb out on an enormous branch I had never tried before. Nervous, to say the least, I pushed out onto the branch and let go. As I dropped, my chest became wedged so tightly between two other branches that I could not breathe.

The spectators sensed trouble and ran for help. My mother came running to save me. Just in the nick of time she freed me with a tremendous push from below. She was furious about my ridiculous trick. It is curious how tree climbing can sometimes be hazardous!

1. Circle all the words that end with the suffix **-ous** or **-or**.

2. Underline the words that tell why I might have died.

3. When you are scared or afraid to do something, you are n__ __ __ous.

4. Would you say that my mother was a professor or a savior? (Circle one.)

5. If you had been me, what would you have done? (Circle one.)
   a. Pulled out a saw and cut the branch off?
   b. Picked an apple off the tree, hoping it was magic?
   c. Called the doctor to say that you have eaten an apple a day and are too young to die?

   d. Other _____

   _____

Suffixes change the root. **-ist** and **-ity** (pronounced as in **city**) are suffixes.

Circle the suffixes and write the syllables in the squares.

Note: Write **-ity** in one square even though it's a two-syllable suffix.

1.	abil(ity)	*a*	*bil*	*ity*	4
2.	organist	— —	— — —	— — —	
3.	druggist		— — — —	— — — —	
4.	security	— —	— —	— — — —	
5.	locality	— —	— — —	— — —	
6.	finalist	— —	— — —	— — —	
7.	festivity	— — —	— — —	— — —	

Now count the syllables in each word and write the number in the margin.
Remember: **-ity** counts as two syllables.

Unscramble the syllables to make a word that fits the meaning.

being held a prisoner = cap
ity
tiv   *captivity*

1. foolishness or lack of smartness = pid
stu
ity

2. one who drives a car = tor
ist
mo

3. an event that causes great harm = ca
ity
lam

4. one who writes novels or books that are not about true events = el
nov
ist

5. one who sings or makes music alone = ist
so
lo

6. liveliness; doing something = ity
ac
tiv

7. a group living and working together = mu
com
nity

Roots and Suffixes: Circle the roots and complete the sentences with the words.

	(drug)store (drug)gist	A _druggist_ is a person who sells medicine in a _drugstore_ .
1.	stupid stupidity	The _____ of our team's play made us all look _____ .
2.	final finalists	All the _____ had a meeting on the _____ day of the contest.
3.	personal personality	It is my _____ opinion that her marvelous _____ makes her fun to be around.
4.	touring tourist	When he was _____ the West, he tried not to look like a _____ .
5.	major majority	The _____ reason the bill did not pass was that the _____ of the people were sick of taxes.
6.	violin violinist	The _____ put her _____ back in its case.
7.	solo soloist	A _____ is a person who sings or plays a _____ in a concert.

Definitions: Find the word that is described and write it in the boxes.

motorist   pianist   ability
tourist   calamity   violinist
majority   security   druggist

1. A person who plays the piano:

2. An event that causes great harm or distress:

3. The driver of a car:

4. The skill or talent to do something:

5. A person who plays the violin:

6. Safety; being secure:

7. A person who travels for pleasure:

Circle the correct words below.

Look at the suffix **-ist** and think about the words we
have used with this suffix. An organist is a

_____ who plays the organ.
You now know that **-ist** usually means "a

_____ who does something."

(motorcyclist) or artist?

1. When you are out driving your car, are you called

a motorist   or   a realist?

2. When you do something foolish, do you blame your

security   or   stupidity?

3. If you have just written a book that is not about real people, are you

a novelist   or   a pianist?

4. Is the town you live in sometimes called

a community   or   a calamity?

5. When you have caught a bird and put it in a cage where it can't escape, is it
said to be in

captivity   or   ability?

6. When something is vital and you cannot live without it, is it

a majority   or   a necessity?

7. If you are a person who fixes teeth and takes care of dental problems, are
you

a druggist   or   a dentist?

Check the headline that matches each picture.

No.	Picture	Headlines
1.		☐ Dentist Gets Fingers Stuck ☐ **Druggist Sells Rare Fingernail Clippers**
2.		☐ Dog Has New Ability (Can Read) ☐ Gas Is a Modern Necessity
3.		☐ First Finalist Wins Piano Contest ☐ U.S. Tourists Visiting Paris by Plane
4.		☐ Fireworks Soar at July 4 Festivity ☐ Frog Held in Captivity by Owl
5.		☐ Security Guards Steal Painting ☐ Violinist Plays Last Concert
6.		☐ Snowball Activity on a Snowy Day ☐ Ability to Tightrope Walk across Falls
7.		☐ Woodworking Artist Wins First Prize ☐ Soloist Sings for the Queen

Yes or No?

	Yes	No
1. Are you a novelist if you have written a book about a castle with dragons?	☐	☐
2. Do you have ability if you make six goals in the hockey game?	☐	☐
3. Do you feel a sense of security when you have your blanket?	☐	☐
4. Are you an artist if you draw on your bank account?	☐	☐
5. Is cleaning your room a fabulous activity?	☐	☐
6. Do your parents keep you in captivity?	☐	☐
7. Can a motorist be a tourist?	☐	☐

Musical Moderato

There was tremendous festivity in Concord as the music contest drew near. Mr. Seltzer, the druggist, was selling tickets. The **judges** were a famous pianist, a violinist, a flutist, and an organist. They would decide who had the most musical ability in town. Raymond Moderato, who plays a marvelous harmonica, hoped to win first prize — a silver toothpick. He *needed* a new toothpick badly!

When the day of the contest arrived, there was much activity at the Music Hall. The **majority** of the players got there early, but Raymond thought that it was a necessity to eat six artichokes beforehand. They limbered up his lips for playing mellow music.

Ray rushed into the Music Hall just as his turn to play was announced. But, alas, calamity struck! Ray did not have his harmonica. He must have dropped it in the hollandaise sauce!

1. Circle all the words that end in the suffix **-ity** or **-ist**.

2. Underline the words that tell what made Ray's lips so limber.

3. When you have a big problem and everything seems to go wrong, it is

   called a c__ __ __ __ity.

4. What did Ray hope to show—his ability or his insecurity? (Circle one.)

5. What would you do if you were Raymond? (Circle one.)
   a. Offer to sing instead because your great personality and limber lips are ready to go?
   b. Pretend you have a headache and ask to play last?
   c. Call the garbage collector to look through your trash can and find the harmonica?
   d. Other _____

   _____

Circle the correct word.

(strangeness?)

or

sweetness?

dampness?

or

dentist?

humorous?

or

hazardous?

stubbornness?

or

slipperiness?

noiseless?

or

reckless?

motorist?

or

novelist?

sourness?

or

festivity?

fabulous?

or

furious?

collector?

or

calamity?

Sharp eyes: Draw a circle around the letters that are different and fill in the blanks.

	fearless fearful A _____fearless_____ rat was trapped and ever after he was _____fearful_____ of traps.
1.	professor protector The _____ was so afraid of cats that he got a large dog to be his _____.
2.	curious curiosity The result of the girl's _____ about the hornets' nest made her less _____ about hornets after that.
3.	humorous humorless Even the _____ old man who never laughed thought my story was _____.
4.	cheerfulness cheerless Grandma's _____ on such a dull, _____ day was a tonic to us all.
5.	humanity humidity The heat and _____ seemed to bother all of _____.
6.	generous generosity The _____ of the rich conductor made us all wish we were more _____.

Choose and add one of the suffixes to each underlined word.

-ous   -ness   -or   -ist   -less

When you write a <u>novel</u>,

you are called a _____*novelist*_____.

1. There was great <u>danger</u> in the wild rapids. It was _____
to go rafting there.

2. His manner was very <u>gentle</u>. I admired his _____ with
the frightened cub.

3. She wore a blouse without <u>sleeves</u>. It was a _____
blouse.

4. If you <u>direct</u> the play, you are a _____.

5. It was getting <u>dark</u> outside. The _____ made it hard to
search for the lost ring.

6. You have a new <u>organ</u>. Now you will become an _____.

7. The label on the blue bottle said <u>POISON</u>. We knew the pills inside were
_____.

Circle the correct meaning or definition of each underlined word.

The prisoner's <u>hostility</u> showed when he spit at the guard.

<u>Hostility</u> means:
    1. a lodging place
    (2. a feeling of hate or ill will)
    3. friendliness

1. The little boy was <u>jealous</u> of his handsome older brother.

    <u>Jealous</u> means:
    1. feeling love for
    2. feeling anger toward
    3. feeling envy toward another

2. It was a hot, muggy day and the <u>humidity</u> was very high.

    <u>Humidity</u> means:
    1. strong, cold winds
    2. dampness in the air
    3. kindness

3. The major's plan to attack the powerful enemy was <u>brainless</u>.

    <u>Brainless</u> means:
    1. well planned
    2. somewhat dangerous but OK
    3. without much thought or planning

4. The <u>emptiness</u> of his old home made Ricardo feel a sense of loneliness

    <u>Emptiness</u> means:
    1. warm and homelike
    2. a sense of being unlived in
    3. a state of being excited

5. The <u>thunderous</u> applause pleased the pianist.

    <u>Thunderous</u> means:
    1. continuous
    2. boring; tiresome
    3. very loud, like thunder

6. The young <u>bicyclist</u> hoped for a cool day.

    A <u>bicyclist</u> is:
    1. one who repairs bikes
    2. one who sells bikes
    3. one who rides a bike

7. Nora's new **job** was the <u>opportunity</u> she had been waiting for.

    <u>Opportunity</u> means:
    1. a chance for advancement
    2. a necessity
    3. a disappointing time

Which word would you use to describe or name a person who:

studious	**jealous**	professor
curious	blameless	dentist
sweetness	collector	silliness

1. — studies all the time? _Studious_

2. — likes to save baseball cards? _____

3. — fixes teeth? _____

4. — teaches college students? _____

5. — didn't do anything wrong? _____

6. — asks about things and is eager to learn more about them?

_____

7. — envies his sister because she's smarter? _____

Puzzle: Find and circle the words you know and then fit them into the spaces below.

The words go across or down the page and can overlap.

```
R E C K L E S S W X
A M N P F A M O U S
X D M Q R S U W V H
Q T Y G B L X O S U
V U B N L B P V M M
P D R U G G I S T I
R B A H I J L S O D
O Q I K L B M Y C I
F R N H G C V V H T
E N L J F D W K I Y
S W E E T N E S S F
S V S W D F G X H K
O S S R Q P L Z J G
R T R O S R K P S S
T R E M E N D O U S
```

R _E_ _C_ _K_ _L_ _E_ _S_ S (not careful)

F _ _ _ _ S (known world-wide)

H _ _ _ _ _ _ Y (dampness in air)

D _ _ _ _ _ _ _ T (person who runs a drugstore)

B _ _ _ _ _ _ _ _ S(without using one's mind; stupid)

S _ _ _ _ _ _ _ _ S (the taste of sugar)

P _ _ _ _ _ _ _ _ R (a college teacher)

T _ _ _ _ _ _ _ _ _ S (fabulous)

31

Famous Joe Crow

Have you ever heard of a bird who was an actor, a collector, an inspector, a director, and a spectator all in one? Joe Crow was all of these and more. He was the most fabulous bird you could ever imagine.

My friend Tom discovered Joe when he was very young. He had fallen from his nest and broken his wing. Tom was a generous boy who loved wildlife so he took the bird to a vet and paid the bill all by himself.

Joe grew to be an enormous bird, but he could never fly. Nevertheless, he was always busy. He was a collector of clothespins. Joe took them out with his beak as fast as Tom put the clothes on the line. When Tom's sister went out to feed the chickens, she learned not to go barefooted as Joe was also a toe collector or tried to be! "Ouch, Ma, Joe's after me!" cried Sis as Joe pecked at her toes.

Joe was a nervous spectator of *all* outside events from car washing to baseball. And wasn't he a director, too? He would sit on top of the car and screech and chatter at the car washers, telling them a thing or two: "Work harder!" "Look out!" "Not me . . . the car, you fool!" Joe was a curious inspector who wanted to be involved in everything that was going on.

When Tom went to camp, Joe became the actor. He put his head under his wing and acted heartbroken. We thought that he had eaten something poisonous, but he was *just* being ridiculous. He really wanted to be a visitor at camp and to see Tom. That bird loved Tom!

Everyone in the neighborhood loved Joe. They would have done just about anything for him. I wouldn't have been at all surprised if Joe had been elected governor — of the neighborhood, that is!

Question Sheet

1. Circle the words that best describe Joe.

   brainless   curious   fabulous

   humorous   continuous   noiseless

2. Write one unusual thing that Joe did.

   _____

3. Circle the main idea of the story.
   a. Joe Crow liked to peck at children's toes.
   b. Crows are curious about some things.
   c. Joe Crow made an interesting and humorous pet.
   d. Tom loved wildlife.

4. Echo the questions. Write your answers in complete sentences.
   Why might Joe have been elected governor?

   _____

   _____

   Why do you think that everyone loved Joe?

   _____

   _____

   _____

5. Circle the smaller word in each word.

   editor   marvelous   director   glamorous

   humorous   visitor   poisonous   collector

6. Supply the correct word from the story.

   a. Someone who shares is _____.

   b. Someone who wants to know why things happen is

      _____.

   c. Someone who collects things is a _____.

   d. Something very large is _____.

The ending **-ture** is pronounced /chur/, as in **nature**.
The ending **-ment** is pronounced /ment/, as in **moment**.

Circle the endings and write the syllables in the squares.

1. agreement	—	— — — —	— — — —
2. improvement	— —	— — — — —	— — — —
3. adventure	— —	— — —	— — — —
4. argument	— —	— —	— — — —
5. furniture	— — —	— —	— — — —
6. departure	— —	— — —	— — — —
7. punishment	— — —	— — —	— — — —

Now count the syllables in each word and write the number in the margin.
Remember to tap!

Unscramble the syllables to make a word that fits the meaning.

a group of persons
making laws and
running the city, state,
or nation
= ment
gov
ern
→ *government*

1. getting better = prove
ment
im
_____

2. homework = ment
as
sign
_____

3. tables and chairs = ture
ni
fur
_____

4. an agreement to meet
at a certain time
= ment
ap
point
_____

5. a penalty for a crime or wrong = ish
pun
ment
_____

6. to make a product = man
fac
u
ture
_____

7. an exciting event = ad
ture
ven
_____

Word Building: Circle the letters that are the same and complete the sentences with the words.

(punish) (punish)ment	When you ___*punish*___ a dog, it must understand why the ___*punishment*___ is given.
1. moist moisture	The air is _____ today. There is _____ in the air.
2. departure depart	They will _____ by boat. The actual _____ time is 7:45 P.M.
3. astonishing astonishment	We all stared in _____ as the huge balloon landed. It is _____ to see such a sight in your backyard.
4. disappointment appointment	Her _____ as head of the FBI was a great _____ to Vic.
5. mixture mix	When you _____ things together, you have a _____.
6. prove improvement	The great _____ in her health will help _____ that vitamins are helpful.
7. arrange arrangement	This _____ is very good. Did you _____ it?

Synonyms: Find the word that means the same as the given word(s) and write it in the boxes.

A word that means the same is called a **synonym**.

puncture	government	advancement
mixture	astonishment	imprisonment
basement	moisture	disagreement

1. Argument:

2. Improvement:

3. Captivity:

4. Surprise or amazement:

5. Dampness:

6. To punch a hole in:

7. Cellar:

Circle the correct words below.

Look at the endings **-ment** and **-ture**.

How do you pronounce **-ture**? /_____/

future   or   (furniture?)

1. When you disagree with your best friend, do you have

an agreement   or   an argument?

2. When you draw a line with a ruler and count the inches, have you made

a measurement   or   a manufacture?

3. When your tire blows out and is flat, is it

a puncture   or   a picture?

4. When a criminal goes to jail, is it

an imprisonment   or   an arrangement?

5. When you can't go skating because the ice has melted, is it

an appointment   or   a disappointment?

6. When your home is three or four rooms in a building where other people also live, is it

a department   or   an apartment?

7. When you break your leg, is it

a fixture   or   a fracture?

Check the headline that matches each picture.

1.
   - [ ] Ball Players Reach Agreement
   - [ ] Captors Have Disagreement over Eagle

2.
   - [ ] New Treatment for Illness
   - [ ] Mistreatment of Animals in Zoo

3.
   - [ ] Actor Takes Picture in Nightclub
   - [ ] Pitcher Has Argument with Coach

4.
   - [ ] Strange Creature Captured
   - [ ] Shipment of Cows Stopped

5.
   - [ ] Cold Wave Hits City: Temperature Falls to Zero
   - [ ] President Has Temperature: Goes to Hospital

6.
   - [ ] Government Assignment for Smart Dog
   - [ ] Homework Assignment Leads to Fame for Class

7.
   - [ ] Yankees under New Management
   - [ ] Farmer Finds Dinosaur Bones in Pasture

Yes or No?

	Yes	No
1. Could you get a fracture skipping in a pasture?	☐	☐
2. Can you capture your shadow?	☐	☐
3. Is playing computer games entertainment?	☐	☐
4. Is it a departure if someone is leaving?	☐	☐
5. Are you glad to have a lot of assignments?	☐	☐
6. When Dad says it's time to go to bed, are you in agreement?	☐	☐
7. Do you live in an apartment?	☐	☐

It's a Dog's Life

When I was a kid, I was often in the doghouse. One time after a disagreement with my mom about doing my homework assignment, I decided to run away. My departure note said, "Homework is punishment. You don't love me. I will never return home. Good-bye."

I didn't really want to go because of the darkness, so I thought of a better arrangement. I would hide in the basement and wait to see if my parents missed me.

Later, I slyly sneaked out and looked in a window. To my disappointment my mother was busy cooking. My open note was on the table. She didn't seem to mind that I was gone forever! I ran to the doghouse to hide with my dog Spooky. Before long I began to feel cramped. This was like imprisonment for me. A dog's life is no adventure I decided, as I sneaked back into the house to do my homework. My mother's only comment was: "Almost time for supper, Nancy."

1. Circle all the words that end in **ment** or **ture**.

2. Underline the words that mean "a farewell letter."

3. When no one seems to notice that Nancy is gone, she feels a sense of
d _ _ _ _ _ _ _ _ _ ment.

4. Did the doghouse hideout turn out to be entertainment or punishment? (Circle one.)

5. If you had been me, what would you have done? (Circle one.)
   a. Called the dogcatcher to report a stray dog?
   b. Sent a telegram to your mother asking, "What's for supper?"
   c. Ordered some new furniture for Spooky's house?

   d. Other _____

_____

Some endings sound alike, i.e., **-able** and **-ible**. In this case, they both say /u-bl/ as in **washable** and **terrible**.

Circle the endings and write the syllables in the squares.

Note: Use the last square for the two-syllable endings, **-able** and **-ible**.

1.	presentable	— — —	— — — —	— — — —
2.	miserable	— — —	— —	— — — —
3.	valuable	— — —	—	— — — —
4.	impossible	— —	— — —	— — — —
5.	dependable	— —	— — — —	— — — —
6.	reversible	— —	— — — —	— — — —
7.	favorable	— —	— — —	— — — —

Now count the syllables in each word and write the number in the margin. Don't forget! **-able** and **-ible** are two-syllable suffixes.

Unscramble the syllables to make a word that fits the meaning.

able to be counted on = pend / de / able → *dependable*

1. worth a lot = val / able / u → _____

2. dependable = able / re / li → _____

3. fantastic = in / ible / cred → _____

4. not able to be seen = in / ible / vis → _____

5. able to be turned inside out = vers / ible / re → _____

6. astonishing = able / mark / re → _____

7. able to be divided = di / vis / ible → _____

Word Building: Circle the letters that are the same and complete the sentences with the words.

(sen)se (sens)ible	Rufus is a _sensible_ dog. He seems to have a lot of common _sense_.	
1.	valueless valuable	The thief did not steal my _____ ring because he thought it was _____.
2.	favored unfavorable	Dad _____ going to the beach today, but the weather was _____ for swimming.
3.	combust combustible	Gas and kerosene will _____, or burn, easily. They are _____ liquids.
4.	depend dependable	Janet is very _____. You can always _____ on her when you need her help.
5.	presented presentable	My report looked neat and _____. I _____ it orally to the class yesterday.
6.	divide divisible	You can _____ twenty by six. However, six is not _____ by twenty.
7.	wash washable	Can you _____ that shirt? I do not think that silk is _____.

Antonyms: Find the word that means the opposite of the given word(s) and write it in the boxes.

Remember: Antonyms are opposites.

miserable	uncomfortable	sensible
possible	valuable	washable
excitable	usable	divisible

1. Calm and quiet:

2. Crazy:

3. Worthless:

4. Happy:

5. Impossible:

6. Cozy:

7. Useless:

Circle the correct words below.

Look at the endings **-able** and **-ible** and think about the words we have used with these endings. The word **breakable** means

" _____ to be broken."
You now know that **-able** and **-ible** mean

" _____ to do something."   miserable   or   (breakable?)

1. | Is a monster show

   possible   or   horrible?

2. | If you are mowing the grass on a nice day and it starts to rain, would you say the weather is

   invisible   or   changeable?

3. | If you have been paid to baby-sit, are you

   responsible   or   remarkable?

4. | Is your new baby puppy

   adorable   or   available?

5. | Is Mom's old tennis racket

   washable   or   usable?

6. | Is a nervous person

   returnable   or   excitable?

7. | If your plastic cup splits down the side when you hold it too tightly, is it

   breakable   or   valuable?

Check the headline that matches each picture.

1.		☐ This Fire Was Avoidable! ☐ Adorable Baby Panda Born
2.		☐ Fans in Stands Are Excitable ☐ Incredible Portrait of Nixon Painted
3.		☐ Supersonic Breaks Impossible Record ☐ Record Awards Given to Winners Tonight
4.		☐ Heavy Thunderstorm Possible ☐ Trained Rabbit Was Teachable
5.		☐ Solar Power Now Usable ☐ Suitable Home Found for Wildcat
6.		☐ Remarkable Inventor Gets Prize ☐ Vote Close in Unpredictable Upset
7.		☐ New Condo Housing Now Available ☐ Tigers' Chance to Win Now Favorable

Yes or No?

		Yes	No
1.	Can a raincoat be reversible?	☐	☐
2.	Are most glasses nonbreakable?	☐	☐
3.	Is fried liver horrible?	☐	☐
4.	Can a dry forest be combustible?	☐	☐
5.	Are your grades in school improvable?	☐	☐
6.	Is your handsome face washable?	☐	☐
7.	Is a fresh quart of milk returnable?	☐	☐

An Unforgettable Cruise

One hazy day Nancy and her dad were cruising on their 36-foot sailboat on Lake Michigan. The weather report that morning was favorable so they headed for Muskegon. About noontime the sun disappeared, waves began to roll, and dense fog set in. Three miles offshore, land was suddenly invisible. It was incredible that the weather could be so changeable.

Dad got out his compass and charts and began to take bearings. How far to Muskegon? It was possible that they were fairly close. Groping their way slowly through the dense fog was miserable. The fog was so thick now you could barely see the bow of the boat. Presently the channel light became visible, and they set their course toward it.

Suddenly a terrible, thunderous sound startled them. Nancy looked up and there, looming behind them in the fog, was the unmistakable shape of a huge steamship. Would the ship see Nancy and her dad in this fog?

1. Circle all the words that end in **able** or **ible**.

2. Underline the words that tell why Nancy and her dad set sail this day.

3. One could make no mistake about what was behind them. The sound and

shape were un ___ ___ ___ ___ ___ ___ able.

4. Was Nancy's dad excitable or sensible about using his compass? (Circle one.)

5. If you had been Nancy, what would you have done? (Circle one.)
   a. Asked Dad to take her home that very minute?
   b. Kissed Dad good-bye and jumped in to swim for help?
   c. Blown the foghorn three times to alert the Coast Guard?

   d. Other _____

Other endings that do **not** sound the way they are spelled are **-tion** and **-sion**. These endings say /shun/ as in **nation** and **mission**.

Circle the endings and write the syllables in the squares.

1. subtraction	— — —	— — — —	— — — —
2. invention	— —	— — —	— — — —
3. confusion	— — —	— —	— — — —
4. suggestion	— — —	— — —	— — — —
5. starvation	— — — —	— —	— — — —
6. expression	— —	— — — —	— — — —
7. explosion	— —	— — —	— — — —

Now say the words aloud in syllables and write the number of syllables you hear in the margin.

Unscramble the syllables to make a word that fits the meaning.

the thing chosen = tion / se / lec > *selection*

Remember: **-tion** and **-sion** say /shun/.

1. a disease caused by germs = tion / fec / in > _____

2. a letter inviting you to a party = vi / ta / in / tion > _____

3. consent to do something = per / sion / mis > _____

4. wearing earth away by water or wind = e / ro / sion > _____

5. a written story = po / com / si / tion > _____

6. careful listening and watching = ten / tion / at > _____

7. preventing waste or destruction of nature = ser / con / va / tion > _____

Word Building: Circle the letters that are the same and complete the sentences with the words.

(collect)
(collect)ion

My uncle has a ___*collection*___ of duck decoys, but I prefer to ___*collect*___ baseball cards myself.

1.
add
addition

I like to _____. Perhaps that's why I'm

so good at _____.

2.
instructor
instructions

After she finished giving the _____ for

the test, the _____ sat down.

3.
elect
election

Do you want to _____ Adams in the

next _____?

4.
express
expression

She used that awful saying, or _____,

to _____ her anger at my leaving so
early.

5.
televise
television

We watched them _____ the *Sesame*

Street _____ show.

6.
starve
starvation

When people don't have food, they _____.

This is called _____.

7.
motion
motionless

After the crash there was no _____ in

the white, _____ body of the truck
driver.

Definitions: Find the word that is described and write it in the boxes.

separation	relaxation	exploration
permission	erosion	television
medication	starvation	celebration

1. A party in honor of someone or something:

2. Not having enough food to eat:

3. The wearing or washing away of earth:

4. Rest or taking it easy and not working:

5. Pills or medicine:

6. The act of searching and discovering:

7. Parting or not being together:

Circle the correct words below.

Look at the endings **-tion** and **-sion.** You pronounce both
/_____/ as in **nation** and **mission**.

Boom!

extra   or   (explosion?)

1. When you are sick, does the doctor give you

   mention   or   medication?

2. When you have done your very best, do you feel

   satisfaction   or   subtraction?

3. When you give money to the Red Cross, do you make

   a direction   or   a donation?

4. When your boss gives you a better **job** with more pay, is it

   a promotion   or   a permission?

5. When you think you've solved a problem, do you have

   a solution   or   a selection?

6. When you had your tonsils out, was it

   an operation   or   a vacation?

7. If you take the train or bus to work, is it your

   composition   or   transportation?

Check the headline that matches each picture.

1.
   - [ ] Exploration of Mountain Hazardous
   - [ ] Election Wipes Out Mayor

2.
   - [ ] Donation Made for Hospital Wing
   - [ ] Location of Gold Found 80 Years Later

3.
   - [ ] Station Needs Funds to Operate
   - [ ] Caution Needed on Dangerous Climb

4.
   - [ ] Attention! Last Day of Sale!
   - [ ] Addition Made to Starting Lineup

5.
   - [ ] Mom Wins Promotion at Police Station
   - [ ] Nuclear Testing Dangerous to Population

6.
   - [ ] Dog Finds Family after Separation
   - [ ] Fly Ball Wins Game

7.
   - [ ] Operation Successful on Hippo
   - [ ] New Flag for Town Hall — A Big Occasion!

Yes or No?

	Yes No
1. Will you be sad if there is no vacation?	☐ ☐
2. Is a birthday a celebration?	☐ ☐
3. When you don't understand your work, is what you feel confusion?	☐ ☐
4. Does a hobo live in a mansion?	☐ ☐
5. Does Mother give you permission to watch television?	☐ ☐
6. Have you ever won an election?	☐ ☐
7. Can an otter give you swimming instructions?	☐ ☐

Secret Expedition

At a certain location in Michigan, there used to be strange happenings in the park when the moon was full. The instruction from adults was to stay away from the park at night. But my friend loved scary explorations. On one occasion when she was visiting, she awakened me late at night and asked if I'd go to the park to observe the statue with her. I did not ask permission but was ready in seconds.

The tall trees were shivering as we entered the dark park. Everything looked silver and strange in the moonlight. Slowly and quietly we began the long walk up to the Civil War Monument. Peering through the shadowy stillness at the statue atop the monument, we suddenly saw a motion. The statue turned silently around and looked down at us. We rubbed our eyes in disbelief! Quickly we stood at attention and saluted it before hurrying out of the park. Had we really seen what we thought we'd seen or was it an illusion?

1. Circle all the words that end in **tion** or **sion**.

2. Underline all the words that make the expedition seem mysterious.

3. When you stand straight and tall to salute, you stand at a __ __ __ __ tion.

4. Would you call this midnight visit an occasion or an occupation? (Circle one.)

5. If you had been me, would you have: (Circle one.)
   a. Checked with the army to see if a soldier was missing without permission?
   b. Gone to get your eyes checked?
   c. Told your parents and promised never to play with your friend again?

   d. Other _____

   _____

Circle the correct word.

valuable?

or

(washable?)

entertainment?

or

punishment?

breakable?

or

returnable?

filthiness?

or

famous?

furniture?

or

fracture?

departure?

or

disagreement?

election?

or

explosion?

selection?

or

subtraction?

capture?

or

manufacture?

Sharp eyes: Draw a circle around the letters that are different and fill in the blanks.

slip
slip(periness)
The _____slipperiness_____ of the floor
made the waiter _____slip_____.

1. protection
protector
My family does not need _____ because my dog is a
good _____.

2. collector
collection
The garbage _____ makes his
_____ every Thursday morning.

3. nature
naturalist
I want to be a _____ someday because of my love of
_____.

4. instructions
instructor
I received _____ on how to drive a car from the driving
school _____.

5. visible
invisible
If something is not _____, or cannot be seen, it is
_____.

6. invention
infections
Her new medical _____ will help fight viral
_____.

Choose and add one of the endings to each underlined word.

-tion   -ture   -ment   -able

When you <u>subtract</u> 3 from 4,

the process is called ___subtraction___.

Note: When you add **-tion** or **-ture** to a word that ends in **t**, drop one **t**.

1. If something <u>suits</u> you well, it is _____.

2. They want to <u>adopt</u> a child. I hope the _____ works out.

3. This cake is <u>moist</u>. It has plenty of _____ in it.

4. Some foods are hard to <u>digest</u>. Eating slowly helps your _____.

5. Your health seems to <u>improve</u> every day. Your _____ means that you can soon go back to school.

6. It was easy to <u>train</u> my rabbit. He is a very _____ bunny.

7. I love to be <u>entertained</u>. A three-ring circus is my favorite kind of

_____.

Circle the correct meaning or definition of each underlined word.

She stared in <u>amazement</u> at the horse nibbling grass in her garden.

<u>Amazement</u> means:
1. enjoyment
2. tremendous fear
3. great surprise *(circled)*

1. In the darkness I saw an <u>illusion</u> that seemed to be a ghost.

<u>Illusion</u> means:
1. an exact copy
2. something unreal or imagined
3. a picture

2. I plan to be a concert violinist in the <u>future</u>.

<u>Future</u> means:
1. day before yesterday
2. last Saturday
3. a time that is to come

3. He does everything the exact way I do it; he is an <u>imitator</u>.

<u>Imitator</u> means:
1. someone who starts a new **job**
2. a mimic or one who copies another
3. the starter of a prank

4. "This food is not <u>edible</u>," she said, spitting it out.

<u>Edible</u> means:
1. salted or seasoned well
2. fit or safe to eat
3. too hot

5. "You are very <u>suitable</u> for this **job**," said the smiling manager.

<u>Suitable</u> means:
1. proper; well-suited
2. ready; on time
3. poorly qualified

6. <u>Pollution</u> of rivers and streams has become a serious problem in America.

<u>Pollution</u> means:
1. too many swimmers
2. too many fish
3. having become dirty and poisonous

7. My mother's new company <u>manufactures</u> computers.

<u>Manufactures</u> means:
1. sells
2. investigates
3. makes

Which word would you use to describe:

adorable   illusion   occasion
future   equipment captivity
connection decision   amazement

1. — someone or something that's very cute? _____

2. — the **joining** of two parts? _____

3. — tomorrow and the years following? _____

4. — being held prisoner? _____

5. — the tools and supplies needed for a **job**? _____

6. — a fine event or opportunity? _____

7. — complete surprise? _____

Puzzle: Find and circle the words you know and then fit them into the spaces below.

The words go across or down the page and can overlap.

```
M I N F O R M A T I O N S T
H M A T I O C L M S P O R V
U P T O W N A D O R A B L E
M O I S T U R E X P U L S X
O S O C H E E R T I C A G P
R E I L P U L Y C G K O S L
W B A M A Z E M E N T F J O
M E N T N R S V Z P H L D S
Q T I M P O S S I B L E X I
B G K S O W A Q Y T U M E O
W C A Q G M U K I O Y S E N
```

C A R E L E S S (not careful)

H _ _ _ R (jokes)

E _ _ _ _ _ _ _ _ N (dynamite's result)

A _ _ _ _ _ _ _ E (cute and lovable)

M _ _ _ _ _ _ E (dampness)

A _ _ _ _ _ _ _ T (surprise)

I _ _ _ _ _ _ _ _ _ E (not possible)

I _ _ _ _ _ _ _ _ _ _ N (facts)

What a Way to Fly!

If you have an adventurous personality, you should try a balloon trip. Filling the balloon with hot air takes about twenty minutes. Propane torches are lighted, and the heat from them is forced into the balloon by a fan. Slowly the gigantic nylon pocket begins to inflate and to rise higher and higher. The basket at the base of the balloon, with enough room for **just** two or three people, is tied to the ground for security while the balloon is being inflated.

At last the balloon is ready to launch. The balloonist casts off the guide wires and the balloon slowly rises. Blasts of hot air from the propane torches control the height the balloon will go; the more heat, the higher the flight. The wind controls the speed and direction of the flight.

It takes skill and ability on the part of the balloonist to keep from crashing into trees and telephone wires. Alertness is a necessity! When a tree looms ahead, a blast of hot air sends the balloon upward and a collision is avoided. Can you imagine skimming the tops of trees and peering down chimneys? This is what is known as "a bird's eye view." Happily the **majority** of flights are without calamity.

A bit later the balloonist spots a green field ahead. By withholding hot air the balloon gradually descends, setting the basket down in the green, grassy pasture. Curious neighbors from the community come from all directions to watch in amazement and to help pack the balloon back into its bag.

What a festive party they have now. The truck that has been trailing the balloon brings treats for all to share. Everyone cheers the magnificent balloon. What a glorious adventure! I wonder if ballooning tourists ever really come down to earth again.

Question Sheet

1. Circle the words that best describe a balloon trip.

adventure   unbelievable   invisible

enjoyable   disappointment   occasion

2. How do you fill a balloon with air?

   _____

3. Supply the correct word from the story.

   a. Safety or being secure is called _____.

   b. Watchfulness or quickness to avoid danger is called _____.

   c. A crash, or two things colliding, is called a _____.

   d. An event that causes great harm is a _____.

   e. Members of a town or a section of town make up a

   _____.

4. Echo the questions. Write your answers in complete sentences.
   How does a balloonist keep from crashing into trees?

   _____

   _____

   What controls the direction and speed of a balloon?

   _____

   _____

5. Circle the smaller word in each word.

   personality   balloonist   festive   majority

   tourists   amazement alertness   noiselessly

6. Circle the main idea of the story.

   a. It takes skill to be a balloonist.
   b. Everyone helps pack the balloon away.
   c. It takes twenty minutes to fill a balloon with hot air.
   d. Ballooning is an exciting activity.

The endings **-ance** and **-ence** have the sounds you hear in **dance** and **fence**.

Circle the endings and write the syllables in the squares.

1. excellence	— —	— — —	— — — — —
2. difference	— — —	— — —	— — — —
3. ambulance	— —	— —	— — — — —
4. influence	— —	— — —	— — — —
5. defiance	— —	— —	— — — —
6. insurance	— —	— — —	— — — —
7. audience	— —	— —	— — — —

Now say the words aloud in syllables and write the number of syllables you hear in the margin.

Unscramble the syllables to make a word that fits the meaning.

a sum or money given weekly = al / ance / low → *allowance*

1. being present at school = ten / dance / at _____

2. something that happens or takes place = rence / cur / oc _____

3. an entertainment of music or acting = for / mance / per _____

4. power or control over someone = flu / ence / in _____

5. a loud commotion or interruption = tur / dis / bance _____

6. taking or receiving something = tance / ac / cep _____

7. refusing to be overlooked or put off = in / tence / sis _____

Word Building: Circle the letters that are the same and complete the sentences with the words.

| (attend) (attend)ance | Do you plan to _attend_ my party? Your _attendance_ would make me very happy. |

1. | prefer preference | I _____ biking to **jogging**. Do you have a _____? Note: The second word divides *after* the f; it is pronounced /pref-er-ence/. |

2. | assist assistance | The Red Cross offers _____ to people who are starving. If you wish to _____ them, you may send them money. |

3. | reappear disappearance | The _____ of the dog's bowl was a puzzle. When do you think it will _____? |

4. | interfere interference | Loud music can _____ with studying. My sister's radio is a great _____. |

5. | annoying annoyance | Buzzing flies can be a real _____. Do you find anything more _____ than flies? |

6. | acquainted acquaintance | I want you to meet a new _____ of mine. We became _____ at camp last summer. |

7. | allowable allowance | I get an _____ every week. Waiting to get it all at the end of the month is _____ in my family. |

Synonyms: Find the word that means the same as the given word(s) and write it in the boxes.

Remember: Synonyms are words that mean the same.

abundance	commence	intelligence
silence	dependence	annoyance
disappearance	elegance	performance

1. Stillness:

2. Plenty:

3. Brain power:

4. Gracefulness:

5. Vanishing:

6. To begin:

7. An irritation or a bother:

Circle the correct words below.

Remember: **-ance** has the sound you hear in d_ _ _ _

and **-ence** has the sound you hear in f_ _ _ _ _.

silence   or   (ambulance?)

1. When something is missing, do you worry about its

   distance   or   disappearance?

2. When someone makes too much noise, is it

   a disturbance   or   a residence?

3. When you obey your parents and do what they ask, is it

   defiance   or   obedience?

4. If you are a soloist in a concert where everyone claps and cheers, are they

   your audience   or   your entrance?

5. If you found the murder weapon with fingerprints on it, do you have

   the evidence   or   the excellence?

6. When your brother keeps teasing you, is he

   an attendance   or   an annoyance?

7. If you can climb to the top of a mountain alone, do you

   have endurance   or   need assistance?

Check the headline that matches each picture.

1.
   - ☐ Entrance to Cave Blocked by Rock
   - ☐ Attendance at Voting Site High

2.
   - ☐ Judge Demands Silence
   - ☐ Judy's Performance Was Excellent

3.
   - ☐ Football Team Runs Interference
   - ☐ No Finance for Gold Medal Swim Team

4.
   - ☐ Acceptance of Check by Mayor
   - ☐ Pets Learn Obedience from Master

5.
   - ☐ Robber Steals Boy's Allowance
   - ☐ Tomato Throwers Are an Annoyance

6.
   - ☐ Dee Dasher: Winner of Long Distance Race
   - ☐ Spectators Cause Disturbance at Car Race

7.
   - ☐ Super Independence Day Celebration
   - ☐ Abundance of Swimmers at Beach

Yes or No?

	Yes	No
1. Is it possible to walk *out* an entrance?	☐	☐
2. Is there a difference between twelve and a dozen?	☐	☐
3. Does your teacher like silence in the classroom?	☐	☐
4. Have you had any experience in skydiving?	☐	☐
5. Can a dry substance be gooey?	☐	☐
6. Is it a coincidence that we were born the same day?	☐	☐
7. Is there an abundance of ice cream in your freezer?	☐	☐

What a Difference a Dog Makes!

Winston was an adorable, playful, black Labrador pup when we got him. He loved to jump on laps and couches, nibble at ears and rugs, give kisses, and nudge elbows. He always wanted attention and an audience. We knew he needed a little guidance, but we adored him anyway.

What a difference a year makes! Winston grew much bigger, but he still had *not* learned obedience. When he jumped up, he knocked you flat on the floor. His kisses were juicy laps across your face, and his nudges to your elbow spilled coffee all over the floor. Winston constantly chewed holes in rugs and branded couches with muddy footprints. Our tolerance began to turn to annoyance!

One day when Winston was left home alone, he got angry. "I'll make a disturbance so that they will come back," thought Winston. When we got home there were only the shreds of evidence! Winston had eaten my homework as well as my mother's bankbook!

1. Circle all the words that end in **ance** or **ence**.

2. Underline the words that tell what Winston liked to do.

3. When one does as he or she is told and obeys commands, it is called

   o__ __ __ __ __ __ __ __.

4. Would you say Winston needed guidance or allowance? (Circle one.)

5. If you had been me, would you have: (Circle one.)
   a. Sent Winston to school to explain about your homework?
   b. Sent Winston to school to learn his A, B, Cs?
   c. Asked Winston to lie down and grow old?

   d. Other _____

The endings **-tive** and **-sive** are not pronounced the way they are spelled. In both cases the **e** has no effect. **-tive** says /tiv/ and **-sive** says /siv/.

Circle the endings and write the syllables in the squares.

1. attentive	— —	— — —	— — — —
2. expensive	— —	— — —	— — — —
3. productive	— — —	— — —	— — — —
4. detective	— —	— — —	— — — —
5. defensive	— —	— — —	— — — —
6. talkative	— — — —	—	— — — —
7. captive		— — —	— — — —

Now say the words aloud in syllables and write the number of syllables you hear in the margin.

74

Unscramble the syllables to make a word that fits the meaning.

a person who solves mysteries or crimes = tec / tive / de   *detective*

Remember: The endings say /tiv/ and /siv/.

1. clever, skillful, and imaginative = tive / ven / in _____

2. having a flaw or not being quite perfect = de / fec / tive _____

3. selective; fashionable = sive / ex / clu _____

4. causing a commotion or interruption = dis / tive / rup _____

5. having an effect or making an impression = im / pres / sive _____

6. easily hurt or upset = si / sen / tive _____

Remember: *i* is short before endings, even if it ends a syllable.

7. helping to improve something = tive / con / struc _____

Word Building: Circle the letters that are the same and complete the sentences with the words.

⟨disrupting disruptive⟩	The wild, _disruptive_ puppy did a good job of _disrupting_ the picnic with his barking and **jumping** about.	

1. expense expensive

She went to great _____ to buy you such an _____ gift.

2. collection recollect

If I _____ her room, it has a lovely doll _____.

3. captive captivity

The enemy was taken _____ and held in _____ for a long time.

4. actor inactive

The old movie _____ lives a quiet, _____ life now.

5. expression expressive

The happy _____ on her face was _____ of the **joy** she felt.

6. impressive impression

He made a great _____ on the young girl, who thought he was a very _____ actor.

7. produce productive

How much wheat does the United States _____ each year? United States wheat farmers are very _____.

76

Definitions: Find the word that is described and write it in the boxes.

massive   decorative   secretive
detective   expensive   native
impressive   creative   active

1. One of the original people of a country:

2. Very large and heavy:

3. A person who solves crimes:

4. Pretty, like an ornament:

5. Costing a great deal of money:

6. Wanting to hide or conceal something:

7. Able to make new and original things:

Circle the correct words below.

Remember: **-tive** and **-sive** say /tiv/ and /siv/.

expensive or active?

1. When something is too big or heavy to move, do we say it is

   massive or native?

2. When you do not want to do something, is your answer

   negative or positive?

3. If you are interested in class and pay close attention, are you

   attentive or expensive?

4. When you write a marvelous story with clay figures to illustrate it, are you

   festive or creative?

5. When a Christmas tree is covered with gold and silver tinsel, do we say it is

   collective or decorative?

6. When you **just** sit quietly and read all day, do we say you are

   active or inactive?

7. If you tell me lots and lots about your friends and family, do we call you

   secretive or talkative?

Check the headline that matches each picture.

1.
   - [ ] Enormous Lion Taken Captive
   - [ ] Lion Captures Bank Robber

2.
   - [ ] Creative Idea Helps Farmers
   - [ ] Creator of Safety Pin Never Known

3.
   - [ ] Expensive Painting Auctioned
   - [ ] Extensive Trip Undertaken to South Pole

4.
   - [ ] Primitive Tribe Discovered
   - [ ] Sensitive Reader Saves Bird

5.
   - [ ] Government Secretive about War
   - [ ] Talkative Girl Gives Secret to Spy

6.
   - [ ] Bicyclist Disruptive at Concert
   - [ ] Detective Arrests Conductor for Train Robbery

7.
   - [ ] Inventive Girl Aids Walkers
   - [ ] Naturalist Helps Save Whales

Yes or No?

	Yes	No
1. Is it expensive to camp in the mountains?	☐	☐
2. Could you keep a firefly captive?	☐	☐
3. If you're attentive, will you hear the story?	☐	☐
4. Is a mushroom massive?	☐	☐
5. Are you a native of your town?	☐	☐
6. Can a necklace be decorative?	☐	☐
7. Is your grandfather a relative?	☐	☐

Undersea Detectives

Excited by our hunt for unusual undersea life, we **jumped** into our **jeep**. With snorkel masks and flippers, we headed for a secluded bay with extensive reefs. Once we were in the blue-green water, attractive schools of purple angelfish, trumpetfish, blue tang, and butterfly fish surrounded us. Giant white sea urchins waved to us from the coral formations. We were a captive audience! My sister poked me and pointed. A massive grouper fish was making faces at us. We searched on through the decorative coral. It was impressive to be among hundreds of midnight blue parrotfish. We were so attentive that we never realized how far out we had swum.

Suddenly there he was — a fierce, ugly barracuda with teeth like saws! I grabbed by sister's toe and motioned to her. Then slowly and silently, so as not to be disruptive, I started back to shore. It seemed miles away.

1. Circle all the words that end in **tive** or **sive**.

2. Underline the words that tell what kind of bay it was.

3. If you make a lot of noise or commotion, you are said to be

   d__ __ __ __ __tive.

4. Would you say that the swim back to shore was active or inactive? (Circle one.)

5. If you had been me, what would you have done? (Circle one.)
   a. Left your sister for bait and swum back to shore full speed ahead?
   b. Tapped the barracuda on the back and told him he needed a good dentist?
   c. Pinched yourself to try to awaken from the bad dream?
   d. Other _____

   _____

-**ify** and -**ize** are endings. -**ify** is a two-syllable ending pronounced /ī-fī/ as in **notify**.

Circle the endings and write the syllables in the squares. Use the last square for the two-syllable ending, -**ify**.

1. ratify		‒ ‒ ‒	‒ ‒ ‒
2. solidify	‒ ‒	‒ ‒ ‒	‒ ‒ ‒
3. modernize	‒ ‒ ‒	‒ ‒ ‒	‒ ‒ ‒
4. memorize	‒ ‒ ‒	‒	‒ ‒ ‒ ‒
5. qualify		‒ ‒ ‒ ‒	‒ ‒ ‒
6. motorize	‒ ‒	‒ ‒ ‒	‒ ‒ ‒
7. finalize	‒ ‒	‒ ‒ ‒	‒ ‒ ‒

Now say the words aloud in syllables and write the number of syllables you hear in the margin.

Unscramble the syllables to make a word that fits the meaning.

to learn by heart =
rize
o
mem
memorize

1. to supply with electric power =
e
lec
tri
fy

2. to put a person in a trance =
hyp
tize
no

3. to understand =
re
al
ize

4. to remember someone upon seeing them =
nize
og
rec

5. to make easy =
sim
fy
pli

6. to point out and tell who a person is =
fy
den
i
ti

7. to add a motor to something =
mo
ize
tor

Word Building: Circle the letters that are the same and complete the sentences with the words.

memory memorize	If you have a good _memory_, you can _memorize_ lots of facts and dates.

1.
visual visualize	If you can see a _____ image of something in your mind, you can _____ it.

2.
simple simplify	When you _____ the directions to something, you make them _____.

3.
realize realization	We came to the _____ that you did not _____ we were lost.

4.
motorist motorized	Could a _____ drive a _____ bike?

5.
critic criticize	A drama _____ will often _____ the actors in the show.

6.
note notify	I sent her a _____ to _____ her of the fire drill on Friday.

7.
apology apologize	When you _____, you give someone an _____ for something you are sorry you did.

Definitions: Find the word that is described and write it in the boxes.

Remember: The suffix **-ify** says /_____-_____/ as in **notify**.

electrify   memorize   magnify
identify   qualify   realize
apologize   simplify   hypnotize

These words are all things you can do.

1. To add electricity to something:

2. To say you are sorry:

3. To make bigger:

4. To learn by heart:

5. To make easier:

6. To point out or name:

7. To show enough skill to be on a team:

Circle the correct words below.

Remember the endings **-ize** and **-ify** as you read the words below.

capitalize   or   (magnify?)

1. When you are sorry you did something, do you

   apologize   or   identify?

2. When you want to put someone to sleep, do you

   criticize them   or   hypnotize them?

3. When you want to learn something and remember it, do you

   magnify it   or   memorize it?

4. When you see someone you know, do you

   motorize him   or   recognize him?

5. When you want to make something new and up-to-date, do you

   modernize it   or   notify it?

6. When you want to make something more attractive, do you

   beautify it   or   jellify it?

7. When you melt something to make it liquid, do you

   liquefy it   or   solidify it?

   Note: *Liquefy* uses *efy* instead of *ify*.

Check the headline that matches each picture.

1.		☐ Doctor Forgets to Sterilize Knife ☐ Doctor Adopts Baby Skunk
2.		☐ Girl Recognizes Picture of Twin Sister ☐ Revolution Breaks Out in Cuba
3.		☐ President Gets Introduction to Queen ☐ Turtle Gets Instructions for Road Race
4.		☐ Experts Realize Bones are Dinosaur's ☐ Election Returns Come in Late
5.		☐ Reading Teachers Simplify Classwork ☐ Class Accepts Invitation to Washington.
6.		☐ Valuable Art Collection Missing! ☐ Art Museum to Modernize Gallery
7.		☐ Star Gets Motorized Shopping Cart ☐ Ringmaster Jealous of Circus Clown

Yes or No?

		Yes	No
1.	Can you liquefy butter?	☐	☐
2.	Can you hypnotize your teacher?	☐	☐
3.	Can the dentist notify me by mail if she wants me to make an appointment?	☐	☐
4.	Will you apologize to your cat if you step on her tail?	☐	☐
5.	Would you recognize your grandmother?	☐	☐
6.	Can you visualize a double-dip peppermint ice cream cone?	☐	☐
7.	Would you electrify popcorn before you popped it?	☐	☐

The Blackfoot Bear Woman

Years ago my family and I used to spend our vacations at our summer camp near a friendly Blackfoot reservation. My brother and I often organized a hike through the woods on our way to get food and mail at the trading post. It was there that we also listened to old-timers tell stories about the past. One story we heard was about a fearsome old Blackfoot woman who, according to legend, could hypnotize people and turn them into bears.

Late one Saturday as we were returning with our provisions, we saw a figure on the path ahead. As we got nearer we realized that it was an old Blackfoot woman. She urgently beckoned to us. We did not recognize her, but it seemed important so we went closer. "I've hurt my ankle and need assistance. Will you help me?" she asked. Was this a trick? Should we help her? Would she turn us into bears? We were so hypnotized by the story of the Bear Lady that we were completely speechless. Even now, years later, we can still visualize it clearly in our minds.

1. Circle all the words that end in **ize** or **ify**.

2. Underline the words that tell what the Bear Woman's secret powers were.

3. If you picture something in your mind, you v__ __ __ __ __ize it.

4. Would you say we might recognize the Bear Woman or notify her? (Circle one.)

5. If you had been us, would you have: (Circle one.)
   a. Asked the woman if she hypnotized bears?
   b. Apologized, but said you were late for supper?
   c. Notified the trading post quickly of the woman's problem?
   d. Other _____

_____

Lesson 12

ti- and **ci-** before an ending say /sh/. The rest of the letters have their usual sounds.

For example: **-tian** and **-cian** = /shan/

-tient and **-cient** = /shent/

-tious and **-cious** = /shus/

Circle the endings and write the syllables.

Remember: **i** before endings is usually short even though it ends the syllable.

1.	musician	— —	— —	— — — —
2.	delicious	— —	— —	— — — —
3.	suspicious	— — —	— —	— — — —
4.	official	— —	— —	— — — —
5.	essential	— —	— — —	— — — —
6.	social		— —	— — — —
7.	financial	— —	— — —	— — — —

Now say the words aloud in syllables and write the number of syllables you hear in the margin.

Unscramble the syllables to make a word that fits the meaning.

someone from the planet Mars = tian / Mar → *Martian*

Remember: **ti-** and **ci-** say /sh/.

1. very good to eat = cious / lus → _____

2. showing distrust = sus / pi / cious → _____

3. showing calm self-control or willing to wait = tient / pa → _____

4. friendly and liking to be with people = cial / so → _____

5. having to do with money and finances = fi / nan / cial → _____

6. careful = tious / cau → _____

7. most important = sen / es / tial → _____

Word Building: Circle the letters that are the same and complete the sentences with the words.

Remember: These endings, **-cient, -tient, -cian, -tian, -cious, -tious,** **-cial,** and **-tial,** all begin with the sound of /_____/.

Mars
Martians

Martians _____ come from the planet
Mars _____ .

1. office
official

The young government _____ has a

new _____ to work in.

2. music
musician

A _____ plays

_____ .

3. finances
financial

My _____ advisor knows all about

_____ .

4. caution
cautious

If you are _____, you proceed with

carefulness and _____ .

5. politics
politician

A _____ is always active in

_____ .

6. electric
electrician

An _____ can fix all the

_____ wires in your house.

7. part
partial

If I give you _____ of what I owe, I

will have made a _____ payment.

Definitions: Find the word that is described and write it in the boxes.

Do you remember what **ti-** and **ci-** say before endings? /_____/

delicious	artificial	repetitious
financial	patient	social
suspicious	martian	essential

1. Expressing distrust:

2. Important and necessary:

3. Not natural but made by humans:

4. Luscious and pleasant tasting:

5. Repeating over and over:

6. Having to do with money:

7. A person having medical treatment:

Circle the correct words below.

Remember: **ti-** and **ci-** before an ending say /sh/. The rest of the letters have their usual sound.

(politician) or caution?

1. If you bake a cake, is it

    delicious   or   repetitious?

2. When you see someone sneaking around the house, are you

    social   or   suspicious?

3. When you have a birthday party, is it

    spacious   or   special?

4. Is doing your homework

    partial   or   essential?

5. If you are an organist and a violinist, are you

    a Martian   or   a musician?

6. When you cross a busy street, are you

    cautious   or   luscious?

7. Is the umpire

    an official   or   an electrician?

Check the headline that matches each picture.

1.
   - [ ] Influential Woman Comes to City
   - [ ] City Mayor Has No Influence on Riot

2.
   - [ ] Martians Land in New York
   - [ ] Musician Plays Last Concert

3.
   - [ ] Sailor Suspicious of Party
   - [ ] Sailor Cautious with Gravy

4.
   - [ ] Antisocial Actor Finds Dark Glasses Essential
   - [ ] Social Workers Find Dogs to Help the Blind

5.
   - [ ] Special All-American Game Tonight
   - [ ] New Hotel Is Spacious and Lovely

6.
   - [ ] Pianist Suspicious of Husband
   - [ ] Patient Comes Home from Hospital

7.
   - [ ] Official Demands Overtime for Game
   - [ ] Author Writes Repetitious Book

Yes or No?

		Yes	No
1.	Does a politician wish for votes?	☐	☐
2.	Is this book repetitious?	☐	☐
3.	Are you cautious when you ride your bike on the highway?	☐	☐
4.	Have you ever shaken hands with a Martian?	☐	☐
5.	Is an ice cream soda luscious?	☐	☐
6.	Do you initial your papers?	☐	☐
7.	Can you cook delicious food?	☐	☐

Martian in the Attic?

In our old house we were used to strange noises, but this was a special sound we'd never heard before. Every night as we got into bed we heard running and scrambling feet in the attic overhead. Had a Martian landed on our house? We finally decided it was essential to find out what was going on.

Our visitor turned out to be an orphaned baby raccoon. Although suspicious of us at first, he cautiously came to get the luscious apple we offered, and we won his friendship. We were patient with him, and eventually he even visited us downstairs. He loved to snatch ice cubes out of drinks and remove lids from delicious-smelling pots. Ricardo the raccoon, our unofficial guest from "outer" space, was a very social fellow.

1. Circle all the words that end in a **ci-** or **ti-** ending.

2. Underline the word that best describes Ricardo at first.

3. If you are friendly and like to be with people, you are said to be s__cial.

4. Would you describe Ricardo's constantly grabbing everyone's ice cubes as repetitious or essential? (Circle one.)

5. If you heard noises in the attic, would you: (Circle one.)
    a. Yell to your mom and tell her that there's a Martian in the attic?
    b. Call on your CB radio that you have bats in your belfry?
    c. Imagine you're only hearing things again and go back to sleep?

    d. Other _____

    _____

Circle the correct word.

invitation?

or

(musician?)

entrance?

or

elegance?

electrician?

or

expensive?

luscious?

or

horrible?

capsize?

or

capture?

secretive?

or

structure?

moisture?

or

Martian?

magnify?

or

capsize?

attendance?

or

ambulance?

Sharp eyes: Draw a circle around the letters that are different and fill in the blanks.

secret~~s~~ secret~~ive~~ Jay is very ___*secretive*___. He only tells his best pal his ___*secrets*___.	

1. questions
   questionable

   It is _____ whether her _____

   will ever be answered.

2. illustrator
   illustrations

   An _____ is one who draws the

   _____ in a book like this.

3. presents
   representative

   Your _____ in Congress _____

   your ideas to the government.

4. dependable
   independence

   The farmers were _____ soldiers when they fought for

   their _____ from the British.

5. patient
   patience

   He was very _____ with his little sister. In most ways,

   he has a lot of _____ with everyone.

6. information
   informative

   Your _____ was very _____.

Choose and add one of the endings to each underlined word.

-ance   . -ize   -ible   -ous   -ist

Funny tricks and jokes told with <u>humor</u>

are *humorous*_____ .

1. Always use a <u>capital</u> letter at the beginning of a sentence. Be sure to

_____those letters.

2. These two sections are not <u>equal</u>. Can you _____ them?

3. You can <u>flex</u> your muscles because muscles are very _____.

4. Sometimes you are <u>allowed</u> to go to the store and use your

_____ to buy candy.

5. One who plays the <u>violin</u> is a_____.

6. If you are very brave and have a lot of <u>courage</u>, you are

_____.

7. When you <u>perform</u> a fantastic bike stunt, your friends cheer your

_____.

Circle the correct meaning or definition of each underlined word.

Remember: **-tious** says /shus/.
         -cial says /shal/.
My grandmother is a patient at the general hospital.

    Patient means: 1. a nurse
                          2. a person being treated
                          3. a janitor

1. The new senator, who was very ambitious, hoped to become president.
    Ambitious means: 1. eager for advancement
                            2. eager for things to stay the same
                            3. prosperous, wealthy

2. We are slowly polluting our environment.
    Environment means: 1. rivers
                            2. basements
                            3. surroundings

3. We now have disposable bottles, napkins, and diapers.
    Disposable means: 1. not having to be ironed
                            2. easily cleaned
                            3. able to be thrown away after using

4. She made a gesture that told me she was tired.
    Gesture means: 1. a horrible sound
                            2. a movement or motion of one's hands or body
                            3. a smile

5. Because I am always moving, the teachers say that I'm hyperactive.
    Hyperactive means: 1. curious
                            2. having good coordination
                            3. excessively active

6. Exercise is beneficial to your health.
    Beneficial means: 1. helpful
                            2. destructive
                            3. not necessary

7. Evaporation occurs when you boil water.
    Evaporation means: 1. liquid turning into vapor
                            2. liquid getting cold
                            3. liquid turning to solid

Which word would you use to describe:

reliable	florist	desirable
nonreturnable	relatives	impatient
beneficial	immovable	patient

1. — a person who sells flowers? _____

2. — all your uncles and aunts? _____

3. — something you want very much? _____

4. — something you bought and cannot take back? _____

5. — something that won't budge? _____

6. — someone dependable whom you can always trust? _____

7. — someone who is restless and can't wait? _____

Puzzle: Find and circle the words you know and then fit them into the spaces below.

The words go across or down the page and can overlap.

```
C A P T U R E Q U A T E A D H
X T P C L I Q U O T A T I O N
B X F O T J U P N L R H V D Z
W C S U G P A T I E N C E K O
F L O R I S T A U E Y O I Q M
C U G A M I O E K Q W N O A S
H L Z G V Y R F B U R F J N D
B X P E N V I R O N M E N T T
K U C O Z G E L G Q J R V A P
R D M U I O S N Y U H E X T C
W L B S R G N X H D V N J B P
T H D N Z T V F X B L C P R J
E P F V L B R H X N D E Y J Y
```

C _A_ _P_ _T_ _U_ _R_ E (to catch something)

F _ _ _ _ _ T (a flower seller)

E _ _ _ _ _ _ R (an imaginary circle around the earth)

P _ _ _ _ _ _ _ E (state of being patient)

Q _ _ _ _ _ _ _ _ N (something that is quoted)

C _ _ _ _ _ _ _ _ _ E (a meeting to discuss something)

C _ _ _ _ _ _ _ _ _ S (brave)

E _ _ _ _ _ _ _ _ _ _ T (surroundings)

A Scout on Firm Foundation

Before it was known to be destructive to the fragile environment, I used to drive my Scout vehicle with four-wheel drive over the dunes on Cape Cod. One day some relatives were visiting, and we decided to explore a section of the Cape called Race Point. I was a capable driver who had been to numerous other beaches so I was unquestionably confident.

Late in the afternoon we arrived at Race Point. Before driving out on the beach, we removed some of the air from our tires. The endless hills and valleys of sand in all directions were spectacular. We drove over and around them. It was perfection until I realized that there were no trails, no water to follow—just sand, sand, endless sand. Now I lost my sense of direction and the ground seemed softer than usual, but the impatient youngsters in the back seat urged me on despite my confusion.

At last we sighted the water and drove out close to it. Suddenly, without warning, two of the tires sank deep into the fine sand, leaving our jeep perched at an uncomfortable angle next to the sea. My most dependable Scout was immovable! My talkative guests grew silent. The sand here was much finer than any I had ever driven on, and I should never have gone so close to the water. I should have been more cautious. Unfortunately the tide was coming in, and I had no wish to abandon my expensive and beloved jeep to a future at sea. Besides, it was getting late and I knew our family at home would be frantic.

So, with a nervous but courageous spirit, I removed more air from my tires and gestured to my riders to climb out. Now with lightened load, I once again climbed behind the wheel. The engine roared—but no motion. Then ever so slowly the Scout began to move. Inch by inch it crept toward firmer ground. Such cheering and celebration you have never seen! Our reliable Scout was saved and so were we!

Question Sheet

1. Circle the words that best describe the Scout.

   reliable   essential   horrible

   victorious   remarkable   valuable

2. Explain why we don't drive on the dunes today.

   _____

   _____

3. Supply the correct word from the story.

   a. Unwilling to wait any longer: _____

   b. Unable to be moved: _____

   c. Members of one's family: _____

   d. Motioned with one's hand: _____

   e. Using care: _____

4. Echo the questions. Write your answers in complete sentences.
   What do you do to a jeep's tires before going out on the beach? _____

   _____   _____

   _____

   Why did we have unexpected trouble at Race Point?

   _____

   _____

5. Circle the smaller word in each word.

   unquestionably   dependable   talkative   transportation

   directions   uncomfortable   perfection   courageous

6. Circle the main idea of the story.
   a. Relatives need to be entertained.
   b. Driving dune buggies can be exciting.
   c. Think and use caution on any kind of adventure.
   d. A Scout is good transportation at the beach.

Matching Relatives: Draw a line to the word that is related.

acquainted   dexterity

dexterous   hazard

fortify   investigation

defective   acquaintance

investigator   fortification

hazardous   defection

---

destructive   recollection

production   impatient

patience   independence

dependent   activity

hyperactive   indestructible

collective   reproductive

Book 8 — Posttest

Word Meaning

Circle the endings in the first list, and draw a line to the **synonym**, or word that means the same, in the second list.

1. essential   celebration

2. improvement   costly

3. luscious   necessary

4. festivity   bother

5. expensive   advancement

6. annoyance   marvelous

7. fabulous   delicious

Circle the endings in the first list, and draw a line to the **antonym**, or word that means the opposite, in the second list.

1. cautious   trustful

2. attractive   reckless

3. captivity   reward

4. hyperactive   horrible

5. disagreement   freedom

6. suspicious   understanding

7. punishment   inactive

Book 8 — Posttest

Can you summarize it? Circle the best answer.

1. Jacky loved to swing from trees, run down hills, climb on walls, jump over streams, and splash in puddles. What kind of girl was she?

   attractive   ambitious   inactive   abusive   active

2. Everywhere along the beach for miles you could see coconut palm trees. What could you say about the coconut trees?

   expensive   assistance   abundance   poisonous   hazardous

3. A few things, such as water, are necessary for people to live. What could you say about water?

   mixture   essential   desirous   emptiness   effective

4. When our teacher's back is turned, Lester can make a facial expression and walk in a way that looks exactly like her. What is Lester?

   idealist   spectator   advisor   realist   imitator

5. The plastics plant dumps all its waste in the river. What is the plastics plant guilty of?

   possession   pollution   permission   protection   production

6. The gymnast can do backbends, splits, side rollovers, and handstands. What is the gymnast?

   sensible   personable   favorable   flexible   breakable

7. This community has many parks and gardens, a lovely new library, a huge arts center, and several new fire trucks. What is true about this community?

   prosperous   obvious   enormous   thunderous   courteous

Book 8 — Posttest

Can you supply the missing word?

---

reservation   conservation   observation   starvation

1. When you want to see planes land, you go to the

_____ tower.

2. When you go to a resort on vacation, you need a _____.

3. People who do not have enough food to eat may suffer from

_____.

4. When you don't like to see our natural environment destroyed, you are

interested in _____.

---

expressive   impressive   oppressive

1. If the heat and humidity are terrible, the weather is

_____.

2. The vast and remarkable Grand Canyon is _____.

3. If you are talkative and imaginative, we say that you are

_____.

---

preference   interference   difference   reference   indifference

1. A dictionary is a _____ book.

2. When two things are not alike, there is a _____.

3. If you like fudge better than caramel, you have a

_____.

4. If you don't care which you have, you feel _____.

5. When the game must be stopped for some reason, it is called

_____.